with best wishes to
the wise woman
of Glastonbury

Satanya Salter
1997

Magical Animals

MAGICAL ANIMALS

Folklore and Legends from a Yorkshire Wisewoman

CLAIRE NAHMAD

Illustrated by Safaya Salter

PAVILION

Especially for Rhys David Bailey

First published in Great Britain in 1996 by
PAVILION BOOKS LIMITED
26 Upper Ground, London SE1 9PD

Text copyright © Claire Nahmad 1996
Illustrations copyright © Safaya Salter 1996

Designed by Nigel Partridge

A CIP catalogue record for this book is available
from the British Library.

ISBN 1-85793-278-1

Printed in Singapore by Tien Wah Press

2 4 6 8 10 9 7 5 3 1

This book can be ordered direct from the publisher.
Please contact the Marketing Department.
But try your bookshop first.

CONTENTS

One

THE BLACK DOG
❋ ❋ ❋

It seems strange that the cheerful, fun-loving dog should be associated with omens, warnings and the angel of death; yet, according to the folklore of many lands, the dog has the ability to see into the spirit worlds. Legend says that dogs howl to warn us to be wary of coming misfortunes, or to let us know that fairies and spirits, ghosts and supernatural beasts, or gods and angels of the forests and hills, are near by. Dogs love to howl at the moon, and when you hear their eerie songs it is easy to look out on the night and imagine that something magical and unseen is slipping by.

Old tales from Romania and Russia tell of the werewolf, that strange beast who appears to be a man or a woman by day, but who turns into a dog by night. The image of the wolf man is very widespread, and the idea that the dog is somehow connected with the human soul is to be found everywhere in folk belief. Why should this be so? The poet Francis Thompson saw God as a huge hound who had to chase our foolish runaway souls so that He could bring them safely to heaven. Perhaps this idea of the dog as hound and retriever, invested with the power of giving

6

chase and bringing something precious back to us, gives us a clue.

In Welsh legend, the story of the hounds of Annwn tells how these ghostly creatures, which came to round up the souls of the dead, were visible to earthly dogs, howling at them in mournful greeting; a dog would let the master and mistress of the house know that a soul was about to be taken up into paradise.

Anubis, the Egyptian dog god, was the custodian of souls and the god of death. He opened the way so that each soul might choose its own path after it had left the earth behind.

Cerberus, grim dog of Roman mythology, watches over the gates to hell. When souls are weighed on the heavenly scales, he waits to see whether they are as light as a feather, or whether they are still heavy and earthbound. If they are, he tosses them back down into the infernal regions, where they have to live out another life on earth. Myths often speak of the earth as being the 'infernal regions', or the underworld; Hell is actually a goddess of the earth and of death, and she too has her pack of dogs.

The celestial dog of the Chinese chases away evil spirits. Hecate, goddess of death and witchcraft in ancient Greece, also had a white hound who knew the secrets of life and death. Some say it represented the moon, whose tides seem to bring the swell of life to earth and then to call them back again, as she waxes (grows big) and wanes (grows small again) in the night skies. The moon is often thought of in folktales as the queen of souls, and dogs certainly seem to worship her!

Dogs can predict the weather. When they frisk about the house, unable to keep still, boisterous and stormy weather is said to be on its way.

An old charm to be said on meeting a white dog goes :

> *"White dog, white dog, go on your way;*
> *Leave good luck with me, and bless this day."*

A black dog can also be addressed like this.

In many lands huge, black, spirit dogs were thought to roam the countryside, waiting for chance meetings with human travellers. The Wisewoman's story is about such a magical dog who haunts Yorkshire. The famous poet and writer Emily Brontë wrote in her diary of her treks with him across the moors. Sightings of the Bargest, as he is called (g pronounced as in 'grass') are still reported to this day.

❧

The Wisewoman's Story
THE TALE OF THE BARGEST

Now this is my story, and this is the way I tell it. It is night, deepest night-time, and the church clock is just striking eleven o'clock in its tower. The stranger tramps down the street to the inn. When he gets inside, he finds the village folk gathered around the great fire roaring in the hearth, talking excitedly. They begin to tell him their news.

'It's a fool indeed who'd cross the moors tonight!' they say. 'Five coaches and three travellers have been waylaid by that wicked highwayman the king's soldiers still haven't been able to catch!'

'Well,' said the stranger, 'I must cross the moor tonight. I've journeyed all the way from the town to bring some medicine for my old mother in the next village, and she needs it before morning'.

'Don't go tonight!' the people say to him. 'The high-wayman will get you! And he isn't the only menace on the moors. There's talk of a great black dog with bloodthirsty eyes as big as saucers, just waiting to carry off your soul! And there's a witch who lives on the moors too! Don't venture out tonight!'

But the stranger tells them again that he has to go and,

with a sigh, he steps out into the wild night. How the wind moans and whistles as he strides out over the desolate moors, and how his heart beats with terror! The first thing he sees is a little old woman with a cheery smile.

'You're in peril, stranger,' she says. 'My dog will walk with you across the moors. Don't look behind you, but keep on walking until you get to your old mother's house.'

Thanking her, the stranger walks on, wondering how she knew where he was bound. But he feels comforted by

the sound of her dog, pad-pad-padding behind him. 'He'll keep me safe,' he thinks.

The second thing he sees is the silvery spirit-woman of a mountain ash tree, getting her rowan buds ready for the first burst of spring. 'That's a strange sight!' he thinks. But he can still hear the dog, pad-pad-padding behind him, so he doesn't take fright. Then suddenly the moon begins to sing, and he hears the moon-maiden up there pour down a crystal voice which echoes all over the moors. 'That's strange, right enough!' he thinks; but the dog keeps on pad-pad-padding behind him, so he doesn't worry.

Here is his old mother's cottage, and here he is going in at the door, and his old mother rising to greet him . . . but . . . 'What is that monster at the door!' she screams. Her son turns round , and sees a black dog as big as a cow, with lantern eyes as big as saucers. And then he knows that it is the Bargest, and that he had walked with him through the world of spirits and wonders, and that it has kept him safe all night.

'Don't worry, mother,' he says. 'That's all right. He's a good dog'. And the Bargest settles itself down across the threshold, wagging its tail.

In the morning, the stranger's old mother is quite well again. What is more, the highwayman has been caught by the king's men. He was talking of how he heard strange singing, and caught his long hair in the twigs of a mountain ash when he followed it, so that he couldn't get away. But of the Bargest there is no sign. Only the witch keeps her secrets, in her little cottage just beyond the point where the stranger met the mysterious old woman the night before . . .

Two

FAIRY FOXES
❦ ❦ ❦

Just think of the old English tale of Reynard the Fox.
Foxes have always been thought of as wily, cunning,
crafty, clever and stealthy: the verb to 'fox' in our language means to pretend, to deceive, to play a trick on
someone. Country people would make a rather grisly
charm of a dried fox's tongue to give them courage and
sharpen their wits.

Foxes were said to be special friends of the fairies, and
would protect the fairy haunts so that the Little People
could hold their midnight revels under the moon in safe-
ty, and dance and sing till dawn. If a human being
approached, the fox would distract the person and lead
him far away. According to old tradition, the fox itself was
often a fairy spirit who had taken animal form for a little
while.

Witches, too, were thought to slip out at night and turn
themselves into foxes at will. The fox was a 'totem' animal
– a very powerful, magical animal, whose physical body
was supposed to be the sacred shape made by a certain
mysterious force or energy. The personality or spirit of this
force took the form of a god, who lived within the fox.

Sometimes it seemed to be just an ordinary animal, but there was also this strange divine power deep within the fox which gave it its fox shape, and which could also take on the awesome shape of a great towering god or goddess of nature. According to country people, a fox could be a witch, a fairy, or a god!

The ancient Egyptians had a similar idea about the magical powers of animals. Their jackal-headed or wolf-headed god (both the jackal and the wolf are cousins of the fox) was Upuaut, the great warrior god who gave cunning and courage in battle. In magical ceremonies he appeared in his magnificent form as half man, half animal, and was called 'he who opens the way'. The Egyptians believed that he could throw open wide the doors which led to mastery and glory, either in sorcery or on the battlefield. We have already seen how the fox stands for courage and cunning, and how its tongue, with which the god inside it would speak the secret magical word to 'open the way', was made into a charm to give wit and courage to the person who carried it. Upuaut could easily have added the fox to his collection of heads!

It is lucky to meet a single fox, but several foxes seen together presage misfortune. If a fox bites someone (luckily a very unusual occurrence), it is said that the person has only seven years to live.

When a sudden shower of raindrops falls out of a clear sunny sky, some people say, somewhere a fox is being married. The people of Japan and Palestine tell the same folktale. A 'fox's wedding' is always lucky and, when it comes, be ready to make three wishes, because tradition promises that at least one of them will come true!

More fox magic involves burying one of the blooms from the foxglove flower under the grass of a fairy ring as the moon rises. If there is a fox living near by, it will send you some silver and second sight to see the fairies. Bury the flower in the same place at noon, and the fox will send you some gold.

Certain families in Ireland, believed to have magical

powers, were said to be descended from foxes. The same story, though less common, can be heard in England and in other countries.

The wisewoman's story is about a similar magical family of foxes.

❧

The Wisewoman's Story
BERENICE AND THE FOX MAN

Now this is my story, and this is the way I tell it. The lord was a proud man, and he dwelt alone in his castle in the wood; all alone except for his cook, his manservant, and his lovely daughter Berenice.

Berenice was always full of frolics and merry laughter. She had hair as dark as the night, and eyes as black as sloes, intelligent and dancing and always shining with fun. She was as light-footed as a foal, and she would often run deep into the woods to climb trees and play games, and sometimes to think her own special thoughts. But she always came back to her father's side before the sun went down.

'What would I do without my own Berenice?' the lord would say to her, for his daughter was his only comfort.

One day Berenice did not come home from the woods. The shadows grew longer and longer, until the moon climbed the stairway of the night and looked down over the lord's castle. Then Berenice came creeping, creeping, pale by moonlight around the castle wall.

'Never be late again!' cried her father. But the next night the same thing happened, and the night after, too.

'Your daughter Berenice has fallen in love with a fox,' said the lord's manservant. 'A great fine fellow, he is, from

the faraway forest. If you don't kill him, he'll take our
Berenice away forever.'

So the following night the lord waited until Berenice
came creeping, creeping pale by moonlight, around the
castle wall. Then he took his musket and walked into the
woods. There stood a great red fox, the finest he had ever
seen. The lord fired once and shot it dead. He went into

the castle to Berenice to confess to what he had done; but when he came into her room, he found not her, but a lady fox, a vixen, lying on the bed. When it saw him, it gave a strange mournful cry and leapt out of the window and down into the deep woods.

The lord felt as though he would never see his dear Berenice again. He thought she must have run away from home because he had been so cruel. He spent all night pacing his room, in grief-stricken silence. Just before dawn, his manservant came to him.

'There are hundreds of foxes surrounding the castle!' he cried. 'They make no move and they sit as quiet and still as the grave!'

The lord rushed outside. The foxes looked at him with a thousand glittering eyes. One of them leapt up and seemed to want him to follow it. The lord did so, pressing on and on for miles into the dark woods as though he journeyed in a dream.

The fox led him to a splendid palace of silver and gold. Upstairs, he found an elf prince lying wounded on a bed, so tall and beautiful and noble that the lord cried out in pity.

'If you would save me, promise me your daughter in marriage,' said the elf prince.

'That I would,' said the lord, 'if she would have you. But she has left me forever.'

As he spoke, the prince's wound was magically healed, and he handed the lord the shot from it, and the lord saw it was from his own gun, the one he had fired at the fox last night. At the same moment, the fox who had led him to the secret palace jumped off the prince's bed, and in a flash became Berenice, as happy and smiling as she had ever been, except more so.

There was great rejoicing in the palace, and the wedding of Berenice and the elf prince was attended by all his fox subjects. They all lived there together, Berenice's father too. And sometimes, on magical nights, Berenice and her prince took on their fox shapes, and slipped out together into the forest to play at fox games by moonlight.

Three

THE JEWEL-HEADED TOAD
❦ ❦ ❦

The toad, according to an old folk belief, bears a beautiful and most precious stone inside its head. While it was safe within the toad's body, the stone was crystal, a jewel which gave the light to the animal's mysterious brown eyes. Great old toads would lose this treasure as they lay dying, and from then on the stone turned dark gray or light brown, and the toad shape of its former owner etched a pattern upon it. It was called a 'toadstone', and to find one of these was very lucky indeed. People had them made into rings or other jewellery, and they would change colour or sweat if their wearer was in danger or if poison was near by. They gave protection from evil witchcraft, and ensured the good health of their owner.

This marvellous stone was said to be connected to the Philosopher's stone, which provided the magical formula for turning ordinary metals into gold and which 'gave forth light'. Noah hung it up in the Ark to 'give light to every creature therein'. This might bring us a little nearer to the heart of the mystery contained in the legend of the toad-stone, because the toad was thought to represent the spirit of stones and therefore the spirit matter itself (in which

there is said to be both light and gold, deeply hidden).

When you look at a toad, you will see that it is easy to mistake him for a stone. Only his wonderful eyes, like strange jewelled mosaics, tell us his real identity.

The toad is the guardian of the 'spirit that speaks from the stones'. We know that the matter within the earth has

great and terrible powers: think of our scientific experiments with the atom and our discovery of the nuclear bomb. Perhaps matter has more beautiful secrets to reveal to us in the future. According to the wisewoman's tradition, we will learn these not through science, but by listening to the spirit voice which speaks in stones, those rocks which make up the body of our planet.

Because the toad is the keeper of so many mysteries, black magicians and witches desired its magical powers. They would be visited by thieves wanting to obtain a dried toad's heart, which served as an amulet to avoid being caught committing crimes. Toads could be invested with harmful power by a black witch, and released into people's gardens to bring them restless nights and bad dreams. A white witch would advise such a victim to bless the toad and make friends with it to break the malicious spell. The white witch knew that no lasting good could ever come to anyone if they treated living things with cruelty. Evil powers, such as acquiring the influence of the Evil Eye, did seem to come to unkind people who killed toads or otherwise made them suffer (an old spell for this was to find nine toads and hang them all up to die); but according to the white witches, all curses came back to haunt their creator. Witches, both good and bad, liked to have a toad as a 'familiar' (a pet animal which was given the same importance as a human companion and with which its mistress had a special magical relationship) because it was an enchanted creature and knew the secrets of the earth. It was thought that the witch could actually take on the shape of a toad and go about the countryside in this secret guise. The spirits of the dead, too, could stay on earth for a while before moving on, using the toad as their 'host'.

If you meet a toad, something good and lasting will shortly come into your life. To see a toad, and especially to become friends with one, is very lucky. It is said that if you offer a gift to the fairies on Midsummer's Eve or Midsummer's Night such as a little silver coin, a small oaten cake, some glass beads or a verse, song or dance that you have made up yourself, then the fairies will lead you to a toadstone, which you should keep forever to bring you luck in love, lifelong blessings, and the ability to see into the future. You might like to keep a look-out, in any case, for one of these mysterious toadstones bearing its pattern of a toad.

If you make friends with a toad and place him carefully in running water (such as a brook or a stream) at midnight, you will according to folk lore become a Toadman or Toadwoman. This means that you will know how to speak to animals, and will have power over them and all living things. You will also be able to attract members of the opposite sex!

✿

The Wisewoman's Story
THE TOAD BENEATH THE TREE

Now this is my story, and this is the way I tell it.

In a faraway time there were two mountain peaks so high that if you stood at their topmost points you could see the strange seas upon the moon. Between these two peaks lay a valley. And in the valley grew an oak tree, so magnificently huge that a magician had transformed it into a tree-castle. He called himself King Tourmalin, and his subjects were the spirits he summoned from clouds and streams, woods and caves, and from the great oak tree itself.

One day King Tourmalin, was in his green tower among the tender spring leaves, when a beautiful young witch came riding by on a snow-white bull.

'Stay and marry me lady!' cried Tourmalin, who had fallen in love with her.

'I want none of you, Tourmalin!' cried the lovely witch maiden. 'I dare say I have more magic in the tip of my nose than you have in all your library of old books!'

'Tell me how to win your heart,' said Tourmalin sadly.

'You must bring me the three greatest treasures your world possesses,' said the witch. 'Among the roots of this tree lives a great toad. A fabulous jewel in its head. If you make it your own, wealth and wisdom will be yours forever. Upon the western mountain peak, only one single flower grows. Its loveliness makes the sun hide his face. If you can pluck it, good health will be yours for eternity. Upon the eastern peak, you will discover the third and greatest treasure of all.' With that, the young witch sped away on her white bull, laughing into the wind.

King Tourmalin put on his mantle of owl feathers, and off he set up the west mountain.

He came to the topmost peak at sunset. There grew a rare and wonderful flower whose leaves outshone the sun in their golden loveliness. Around it in the air hung a perfume which might have fallen from the stars. King Tourmalin plucked it, and turned his steps to the eastern mountain. When he arrived there, nothing was to be seen, only the rose pink light of day as the dawn broke, and the smiling sun coming up over the rim of the world. As he watched it, Tourmalin felt a singing in his heart, as though a little bird fluttered joyfully there. He waited all the day, but still there was nothing to be seen. Sadly he went home, hoping that the witch would be satisfied with only two of the treasures.

When he reached his oak-tree palace, he took a sword and climbed down into the cellars where he began to hack through the roots, travelling deeper and deeper underground. At last he came to a great cave, where two enormous eyes like old gold set in softly shining brown marble blinked out at him.

'I am the toad beneath the tree. Have you come to kill me Tourmalin?' said a soft, heavy voice.

'I have' said the king, raising his sword.

'Long have I lived in the dark,' said the toad. 'Here I have sat for many a year, guarding your castle and blessing it with my magic. All your magic is mine. I am the beating heart of your craft, the voice of your spells. But kill me if you must.'

'I want the jewel,' said Tourmalin. 'The one in your head.'

'That jewel is wondrous,' said the toad. 'All the magic of the earth is in it. It would make our little planet into a star, and you, Tourmalin into a god. But if you let me live, I will bring you the spirit of wisdom, for that hidden jewel is my soul, and only I can hold it.'

Tourmalin felt ashamed suddenly, and threw away his sword. 'You are greater than I, yet you speak humbly, and would never harm me,' he said kindly.

'I am dying,' said the toad. 'Nothing can save me except the flower from the western mountain.'

Tourmalin immediately took the magical flower from beneath his cloak and gave it to the toad to eat. As the toad swallowed it, the bird began to sing in Tourmalin's heart again. In a flash of enchantment, the young witch was at his side.

'You have done well Tourmalin,' she said to him. 'Far better than I expected! I am ready to become your bride!'

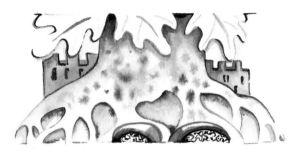

'But . . . I never found the third treasure, lady,' stammered Tourmalin. 'The one that was the greatest of all.'

'Yes you did,' the witch maiden answered merrily. 'The third treasure was Love, and you found it on the eastern mountain and brought it back home with you!'

So Tourmalin and the witch maiden were married; and all their days they learned from the toad beneath the tree the wisdom he brought them from the secret depths of the earth.

✤　　✤　　✤

Four

THE SACRED SWAN

❧   ❧   ❧

Richard the Lionheart is said to have brought the first swans to Britain from Cyprus after the Third Crusade; but there are so many old Celtic tales about them (the Celts were an ancient people who lived in Britain before Christianity became the national religion, long before Richard the Lionheart's time) that it seems that swans may always have lived in the United Kingdom. In Ireland Fionnula, daughter of King Lir, was transformed by sorcery into a swan and condemned to wander for hundreds of years over the lakes and rivers of Ireland until St Patrick brought Christianity to the land. So in history, folklore and poetic myth, swans, royalty and Christianity are constantly linked. Today swans are royal birds, and live under the protection of the King or Queen. With their serenity and their pure white plumage, they are to many people a symbol of Christ.

In the northern hemisphere the swan has always been considered a sacred bird, beloved of the gods. According to an old tradition, swan's eggs can only be hatched during storms, when thunder and lightning crash ferociously over the nest. Only this cosmic power can break the eggshell

and bring forth the cygnet.

In Scandinavia the swan was a totem bird, representing the power of the great god Frey; it was associated with the white cirrus clouds from which his sky chariot was formed. In Germany the great warrior goddesses or Valkyries, who accompanied soldiers to war and inspired them to fight bravely, were swan maidens; they summoned the slain warrior souls to Valhalla, the northern paradise. In Finnish myth, a dangerous river with black billows protects the gate to the underworld, the land where all magic and enchantments and the secrets of life are known; upon this river, as its guardian, lives the mystic swan of King Tuoni, lord of the nether realms. Here, once again, the swan is the keeper of magical powers.

In Greek myths, Apollo's chariot was drawn by swans when he flew north to the land of everlasting youth, and Apollo himself, with his twin sister Artemis, was born to the goddess Luto after the all powerful god Zeus had visited her in the form of a swan. The story of Leda and the swan tells how the god Jupiter visited the beautiful Leda as a swan. Their union produced two eggs: one hatched into the heavenly twins, Castor and Pollux, the other into Clytamnaestra and Helena.

It is unlucky to kill a swan: according to many myths, the swan is a human soul which has chosen to be re-born in this divine shape. Because of this, any swan-slayer also symbolically kills himself and, it is said, will actually die within the year. This connection with human beings appears again in Australian aboriginal myth, where black swans are the bird forms of a human tribe who found sanctuary on the top of a mountain during a great flood, and became black swans as the water reached their feet. The idea that human souls and swans are connected appears over and over again in myth, legend and fairytale.

One of the most poignant images in swan mythology is that of the dying swan singing, having been silent throughout its life. The writer and traveller Erman said of the swan, *"This bird, when wounded, pours forth its last breath in notes most beautifully clear and loud."*

The notes are said to resemble those of a violin, though purer, higher and sweeter than any earthly instrument. As it is dying, the swan allegedly glimpses paradise, and gives forth its song of joy because its soul is drawing nearer and nearer to the heavenly worlds. Some say this hauntingly lovely 'swan song' actually pours down to earth from the 'jewelled meads of Paradise'. So it is fitting that there is a celestial swan, on the wing in the heavens, marked out in the stars. Its name is Cygnus, the great magical white swan which among other things is supposed to summon a hero

or heroine to save a country in its direst need.

When you see white cirrus clouds, predicting fair weather, they represent swan phantoms which bring blessings, and you can make a wish for your future. Swans are magically connected with the land of everlasting youth, the 'enchanted western isles' where all health and happiness dwell; hence the old charm to be said on seeing a swan,

'White swan , white swan, lady or lord;
bring me joy and good health and wine for my board.' (table)

Falling snow was once thought to be the mystical feathers of swans who lived in paradise, and so the same charm can be said during a snowfall!

To dream of a swan is a sign of the White Goddess, the queen of all nature and of human souls. It foretells beautiful experiences and spiritual delight, and indicates that the dreamer has 'soul-power', the power of wisdom, dreams and prophecy, and the power of creative imagination which can make its secret visions come true.

❧

The Wisewomans's Story
THE SWAN MAIDEN

Now this is my story, and this is the way I tell it.

Young Wilkie was walking towards the forest pool, feeling sad and sorry. He was a poet and a dreamer, and he did not seem to be able to do farm work well like the other men in the village. They laughed at him, and the farmer sent him packing, and told him his songs and his music would never earn him an honest crust. None of the village girls would marry him because he had no money, and so Wilkie was all alone. He often came to the forest pool to set his verses to music, and there he would whistle and pipe away his sorrows.

Yet today, someone was already at the side of the lonely

forest pool. A beautiful young maiden in a flowing white gown was stepping into the clear water to swim. She was so lovely that Wilkie fell head over heels in love with her. He crept to the edge of the pool, thinking he would say hello, when he noticed that a fine and handsome feather robe, white as snow and in the shape of a swan, lay upon the bank. Wilkie realised that this magical young girl was a swan maiden, of whom he had heard tell in old tales, and for whom he had often strung verses together, because swan maidens sometimes visited him in his dreams. So he seized the feather robe and hid it under his coat.

When the swan maiden came out of the water she saw Wilkie, and in a fright she tried to find her robe. She knew that, once she put it on again, she would fly off and be free in the shape of a swan once more. But she fell in love with Wilkie, the poet and the dreamer, and she didn't mind that she couldn't find her robe. They went home together and were married. It didn't matter that Wilkie had no money, because every month at full moon the swan maiden returned to the lake, and the spirit of the water would pour

jewels and pearls and silver and gold into her lap. So she
and Wilkie prospered, and Wilkie made up his poems and
songs and dances, and she sang for him, and they were
wonderfully happy. They had three fine children, every
one a beautiful daughter.

One wild snowy night Wilkie went to help the village
men rescue some sheep. It was so cold that he thought he
would put on the hidden feather robe, as he believed it
was the only thing that could keep him warm on such a
bitter night.

'It won't matter, after all this time, if my wife sees it
again,' he thought. But as he put it round his shoulders, his
wife came in to see him off and bid him take care. She
stared at the feather robe . . . and in a trice she had put it
on, and all he saw of her was a beautiful and graceful swan
which flew out of the open door into the darkness and the
flurrying snow.

Wilkie grieved for his swan maiden. But he was comforted throughout his remaining years by his three daugh-
ters, one of whom danced like sunlight upon the water,
one of whom sang like a voice in a dream, and the last of
whom could play the harp and the fiddle like a fairy
woman. Three rich suitors took them to wife, and Wilkie
went to live with the youngest, who helped him make
music for his verses. But he never forgot his swan maiden
love, and he spent all his days by the forest pool, sighing
and seeking her reflection in the water.

Five

ANGELIC BEES

❦   ❦   ❦

Wonderful stories are told about bees in folklore: bees are little winged messengers from paradise and servants of God. While many other animals are associated with the fairies, bees are definitely angelic!

A Welsh legend tell how bees were white when they lived in heavenly realms, and white bees flew about the Garden of Eden with Adam and Eve; but, when Eve decided to take the hard path of self-knowledge and Adam followed her, the bees fell from paradise as well, and their furry coats turned from angelic white to brown and black. They were entrusted with the sacred task of making wax for the altar lights so that mortals could worship God and the nature goddess, and they make honey for our delight and good health, and to remind us of paradise while we struggle down below on earth. There is something rather magical about honey, because it contains all the vitamins and minerals in just the right tiny quantities that the human body needs day by day.

Bees worship God and the nature goddess as they go about their work, humming anthems of praise all day long. If you listen closely on a summer's day, you might agree

that several bees buzzing in unison sound something like a fairy church organ! This buzzing becomes very intense on Christmas Eve, when bees hum the Hundredth Psalm in their hives on the stroke of midnight in joyful welcome and honour of Christ's birth.

It is very unlucky to kill a bee; in doing so, you are striking out at one of the angels in paradise. Bees have within them the wisdom of the angels and the spirit of the earth, and so they must not be bought or sold as goods. A borrowed or given swarm will fare better than one sold at the market, unless payment is made in gold, the metal of divine purity. Bees like to be owned by both a man and a woman, preferably of different households, because they belong both to the God and the Goddess.

Bees have knowledge of the future and of secret things. They cannot thrive if there is spite or ill-feeling in the household, or if they themselves are the subject of an angry quarrel. They decline and die, or fly away. They hate blasphemy and swearing, as they know that these habits are a direct evocation of the powers of evil. They may attack the swearer in order to chastise him. Bees are emblems of purity, and it is said that virgins, and the pure of heart, can walk through a swarm of bees unharmed.

It was once the custom to 'ring' or 'tang' bees when they swarmed by banging pans, bells, gongs, or fire irons so that they would settle quickly without flying off too far. If the 'tanging' did not take place the owner of the swarm was considered to have lost it if the swarm settled on someone else's land. While the tanging continued, he could follow wherever the bees led without being accused of trespass.

Bees brought messages from God and the angels to tell people that their souls would soon be needed in heaven. They would do this by suddenly deserting the hive or swarming on the dead branch of a tree, or on rotten wood. If a strange swarm suddenly appeared in a garden or back-yard, and was not claimed by its original owner once it established itself there permanently, it foretold a birth or a death in the family within the next year.

A watch was kept on the first swarming after a bee keeper's death, because this indicated whether or not the new master or mistress had been accepted by the bees. The omen was good if the swarm was easily taken, but if there were problems and the bees swarmed on dead wood, it was said that the new owner would not live long. If the

swarm disappeared and was lost, then the dead man had called them to himself.

A strong bond of sympathy and love is thought to exist between bees and their keeper. In the past the bees were told all the news of the family, births, marriages, separation, reunion, deaths; indeed all the joys and sorrows of the household. If they were not kept informed they would leave, never to return. The most solemn event of all was the death of the keeper himself; his eldest son or daughter, or his widow, had to strike the hive three times with the iron door key and say, 'The master is dead.' Hives went into mourning by having pieces of black cloth tied to them; they were turned around when the corpse was carried out of the house. A sample from every dish served at the funeral feast had to be saved and given to the bees, and one of the former keeper's personal possessions was also presented to them.

Bees were the guardians of death, one of the earth secrets. Human souls were believed to take the form of a

bee for a short time after death. Sometimes the bee was seen as an angel of death, gradually guiding the human soul home to paradise.

When a bee flies into the house, it is a sign of good luck and of the imminent arrival of a stranger; but the luck is destroyed if the bee is injured or chased out of the house as it must leave of its own accord. A bumble bee on board ship is a very lucky omen, especially if the vessel is at sea. If a honey bee alights on your hand, money is coming to you; if it settles on your head, you will rise to greatness. A bee flying round a sleeping child is its 'good fairy', bringing gifts of happiness, wealth and a pure heart.

According to folk lore it is an omen of war if bees are idle, or miserly in producing honey. They are said to nest on the roofs of houses where the woman is strong and dominant. Bees love children, and will not sting them unless severely provoked. Yet even in bee stings there is some good, for they have been proved to be an excellent medicine for rheumatism. In mythology, bees nourished

the god Jupiter; they also fed the great bard Pindar in his infancy. The priestesses of Ceres (goddess of wheat and nature) were bees. The Greeks consecrated them to the moon, but they were also associated with the planet Venus (who herself is linked with the moon).

If you dream of a bee, expect to 'come into your own' whether through money, position in life, or by the blossoming within you of some art or craft, because the bee is a sign of royal succession, a time of rewards, fruition and success.

❧

The Wisewoman's Story
THE TRUE TALE OF SAMUEL JONES

Now this is my story and this is the way I tell it.

A tale is told of a certain Mr Samuel Jones, who lived in Bath. He loved his bees so much that he was always talking to them and telling them things; and he said they whispered back to him, and that if he had any wisdom, and knew many strange secrets, then it was because the blessed little bees had taught him so well.

Mr Samuel Jones would sit in a chair before his hive and

tinkle a bell. Out would swarm the bees, clustering all over him in the greatest delight, loving him as much as if he were a queen bee. Three days after he died at the grand old age of eighty three, his neighbours came to lay flowers upon his grave. They found that it was buzzing from head to foot with Mr Samuel Jones's very own swarm of bees, who were thought to be humming an anthem of praise so that Mr Samuel's soul could rise straight away to heaven. And by the light that shines, this story is true!

Six

THE FLEET HARE
❧   ❧   ❧

Hares are sacred to the moon, who was always seen as the mother-goddess. The Hindus say that the outline of a hare is distinctly visible upon the moon's surface and with the help of a little imagination it is possible to see the hare shape upon the face of the full moon. The ancient Chinese also believed that there was a hare in the moon. At the festival of the moon which always took place on the fifteenth day of the eighth month (in August or September, depending on the date of the Chinese New Year), women and children celebrated by buying little figures in the shape of a white rabbit, or a helmeted soldier with the face of a hare. To these figures some fruit would be offered up. When the moon in which the sacred hare lived rose above the rooftops, more offerings would be made of choice fruit, sweet cakes, and a sprig of red amaranth. This was how they honoured the moon goddess and the spirit of the moon hare. The moon hare is said to make the drug of immortality and give it to the heavens and to the cycles of nature here on earth.

The idea of the mother goddess being associated with the hare appears again in the mythology of the Algonquins,

North American Indians or Native Americans. Here, after the Great Flood has swept everything away, Michabo the great Hare goes forth to create the world anew.

In Europe the hare is sacred to the goddess Eastre, goddess of the east, the rising sun, of fertility and the returning spring. Like the Chinese moon hare, it embodies the spirit of immortality and of the spring which is eternally reborn. The Easter hare lays Easter Eggs to celebrate the idea of birth, children and everlasting youth.

Witches were said to transform themselves into hares and run all night in this guise. Such enchanted hares could only be shot with a silver bullet (silver is the metal associated with the moon and would of course have a strong influence on magical hares). This belief has persisted for many, many hundreds of years in Europe.

To meet a white hare is unlucky because these animals are said to be the 'soul shapes' of young girls who have been deserted by their lovers and die of grief. They assume the form of a hare in order to haunt their betrayers.

To meet a black or brown hare is lucky, although if one

crosses your path you are well advised to go home and start out on your journey once again to avert ill-luck. Fisherman will not set out to sea if they spy a hare because they believe that the animal is issuing a warning. The word 'hare' must not be spoken on board ship, nor will miners speak it underground. Fear of their association with witches seems to persist in some countries: it is said to be unlucky if a hare crosses the path of a wedding procession or jumps on a wall. To be 'hare shotten' was to suffer from a hare-lip (split at the top, like a hare), said to be caused by a mother meeting a hare on the road shortly before giving birth. A hare racing down the high street of a village was a warning against fire, and a dream of a hare told of secret enemies, and of death and misfortune on its way to a member of the dreamer's family.

These omens of doom belong to latter day attitudes towards the hare and towards the powers of women and witchcraft, which were always seen as evil and malicious. This unhappy view is beginning to change today, and we can return to earlier and blither beliefs, which still saw the hare as a divine and sacred animal of the mother goddess, a sign of happiness and renewed hope.

A hare's foot carried around one's neck was supposed to ward off rheumatism. This is a healing charm to say if you should be suffering from ill-health:

'Hare spirit, swift as lightening
The devils in me need affrighting
Brightest angels in high heaven
Fright them from me seventy-times-seven
Now do they reside in you
Run, Run, hare spirit, till fall of dew.'

If you dream of a hare, you may no longer expect the dire and dreadful fate which was foretold in recent folk belief, but rather look forward to the discovery of a mystical trail of new beginnings which will lead you to spiritual and material treasure!

❧

The Wisewoman's Story
THE WITCH HARE
Now this is my story and this is the way I tell it.

There was an old dame in Cleveland who was a good woman, having knowledge of herbs and the sort of wisdom which encouraged her neighbours to call on her for healing and advice. Some folk called her a witch, but she would have no quarrel with them, saying,

'Truth is truth, my dears; and you shall know who I am by the fruits of my labour, not by my roots!' – by which she meant that people ought to look at what she did, rather

than attempting to judge her by what they could not see, with suspicion and tittle-tattle.

One day a great rough farmer came to call. The old lady was laid up in bed at the time, having suffered some injuries the night before.

"I've come to arrest you in the name of the king, witch!" he said gruffly. 'I spied a hare going after my young

saplings and I took a shot at it with some bits of silver but-
ton for bullets, and down it went for a minute and ran off
shrieking. Now everyone knows you can only shoot a
witch hare with silver bullets, and that afterwards that very
witch in her human form will be found abed in sore afflic-
tion. And here you are!'

'Foolish man that you are, Gilbert!' said the old lady.

'Don't you know that when you harm an animal, you harm
yourself? Now it's quite true that I was harmed by your
bullets last night, though not in the way you think. I took
the injuries that should have been yours on my own self,
because I knew you were a poor ignorant man without any
knowledge of the secrets of life. But since you've come to
reclaim what is truly yours, I can say no more to help you!'

With that, the old dame got up from her bed, fit as a fiddle, and the farmer ran off in a fright. When he had gone the old lady opened the door and sent her spirit out into the wilds to find the hare. Soon it came limping to her house door, whereupon she took it inside and nursed its wounds.

As for the farmer, a trestle hanging from the barn roof fell on him the very next day, and he was in a bad way for many weeks. The old dame came to him with her herbs and gradually got him well again. He never shot another creature and if he ever heard anyone speaking of the old dame as a witch, he would frown and say, 'Hush, hush There are many secrets in this life we know nothing about!'

As for the good old lady, she got on with her healing and her good works. But sometimes, when the night was fine, she would let her spirit run about in the wilds with her friend the hare, and know what it was like to be young and free and lithe of limb again.

Seven

THE ENCHANTED CUCKOO

❧　❧　❧

The Cuckoo is a bird of the earth goddess, and herald of the returning spring. She begins to sing just after Easter, and is associated also with the sacrifice necessary for the rebirth of the spring and the summer. The idea that some sort of sacrifice had to be made so that light and life would return to the earth is a very ancient one. This is why according to folklore the cuckoo lays her eggs in the nests of other birds. The little nestlings fall to the ground to die because the large and strong baby cuckoo pushes them out as it grows. This is the sacrifice demanded by the cuckoo as the bird of the earth goddess, the bird of life and death.

As the bird of life, the goddess flies as the spring cuckoo; as the bird of death she flies as the grim hawk of winter. Folklore tells us that the cuckoo turns into a hawk, its earthly shape in the winter, while the ghost or spirit of the cuckoo flies for protection into the fairy halls deep beneath the earth to wait for spring to come again. Because of this belief, the cuckoo is also thought of as a fairy bird.

North country people used to declare a holiday on the day when they first heard the cuckoo sing. Its song was believed

to be the magical heartbeat of the earth reviving after her winter sleep, musical and melodious to the ear. The enchanted cuckoo song brought the bounty of the spring time and the promise of the summer harvest in August, at which time, the cuckoo leaves the land and flies south.

It is thought to be lucky to hear the cuckoo call, especially on 28 April the day of the Cuckoo Feast. To hear it after old Midsummer's Day (5 July) though, was a warning rather than a good omen.

In Cornwall the Cuckoo Feast commemorates the day upon which the cuckoo brings spring to the land. In many legends the cuckoo is seen not only as herald of the spring, but the spirit of spring itself. In Sussex the earth goddess appears in the guise of an old woman who has charge of all the cuckoos and controls the seasons and the weather. She releases her cuckoos at Heathfield Fair on 14 April, but their numbers depend upon her good humour. If she is in a bright mood she sends forth many cuckoos, but if her temper is bad, only one or two are allowed to fly off. A large number of cuckoos signifies a warm and bountiful spring but just a few foretell a cold and late spring which will eventually yield a miserly summer harvest. The old woman's mood seems to be inspired by the way nature and her spirit have been treated. If we accord them respect, she is pleased; if not she is angry.

Cuckoos are rain birds as well as fairy birds, and when they call persistently warm nourishing rain is said to be imminent. In Scotland the arrival of the cuckoo is said to be announced by 'gowk storms', and the cuckoo itself is referred to as a 'gowk'. In England the cuckoo is often called the 'Welsh ambassador', perhaps because in ancient times the cuckoo was a bird of great mythological importance to the Celtic peoples who inhabited Wales.

An old cuckoo lovespell, popular in bygone times in Europe and America, predicts that if you should hear the cuckoo call in the dark hours of the early morning, when the moon is new, you will have happy love affairs; if the moon is full when you hear the early morning cuckoo, you will marry early; if it is waxing (growing to full), you will find a new love, if it is waning (gradually disappearing night by night), you will be engaged for a long time before you eventually marry; but if you hear the cuckoo call in the dark of the moon (the day or two just before the full moon when it completely disappears from view) then beware! You will have a strange, moody, passionate lover, full of dark thoughts!

If you hear the cuckoo calling to your right, folklore says she is telling you that you are in luck! If she calls to your left, she is giving you a warning to take care. If, when you first hear her call, you are standing on grass, soil or soft ground, the omen is good; but if you are standing on hard, barren ground, or on a pavement or a road, you need to say this little charm:

> *'Cuckoo spirit, fly hither,*
> *Chase evil luck thither!'*

If you have some money in your purse or pocket when you hear the cuckoo call, especially if it is the first time in the year, turn it over and say this money charm:

> '*Lucky coins, now I count thee,*
> *Cuckoo-fairy bring me bounty!*'

❧

The Wisewoman's Story
THE TRUE TALE OF FARMER MOFFAT AND THE CUCKOO

Now this is my story, and this is the way I tell it.

One freezing, snowy, blustery evening, when you would think it was deepest winter although it was early April, Farmer Moffat of Towdenack in Cornwall decided to invite some friends round for a bite of supper. They all sat round the blazing fire, hearing the wind moan and scream outside, and watching snowflakes whirl against the windowpane.

'What weather this is!' said Mrs Butterwick. 'Will spring ever come again?

'Now let's do what they did in the olden times,' said Mrs Moffat, who was very wise. Hadn't her family lived in Cornwall since goodness knows when, and wasn't Cornwall an old Celtic country, full of magic and wonders? 'We'll drink a toast to the Great Mother of all things, and ask her to change the weather!'

So Farmer Moffat brought out his finest port and filled all their glasses, and the company raised them and drank in honour of the Great Mother. The fire leapt up and did a dance, and farmer Moffat seized the biggest log on the hearth and cast it into the flames.

Lo and behold, out from the hollow log flew a cuckoo, fluttering around the room and warbling its soft notes! Mrs Moffat nodded to herself, and let it out of the window.

'Thanks be to the Great Mother,' she said.

The very next day dawned as still and shiny and warm as could be, and from then on it was the best spring anyone could remember.

And by the light that shines, this story is true!

❧   ❧   ❧

Eight

THE CELTIC HORSE

❖ ❖ ❖

The horse has always been regarded as a guardian spirit of its owner, and this is easy to understand when we reflect that, until recently in history, we depended on the horse to plough the fields whose crops would feed us, to carry men into battle, and to provide us with postal communication and transport. Horses have been sacred from the beginning of time to people across the world. Many people made annual sacrifices of the horse to their gods, among them the ancient Romans, the Norsemen and the Vedas of India. The horse was seen as a symbol of the great god, the sun.

There are many marvellous tales of horses in world mythology. Epona the Celtic goddess protected ponies and horses and appeared in the form of a horse. Odin galloped across the skies on an eight footed horse which was sometimes white, sometimes dappled grey. Lady Horsehead, a Chinese goddess, bears her horse's head because a horse fell in love with her and, upon being slain by the lady's father, it magically resurrected itself and carried her off. The lady left her strange spirit lover to live in the heavens, but her soul remained in love with the horse,

and so she assumed her horse's head. The Chinese god of hell sends out a spirit in the shape of a horse to collect souls when it is their time to die, and to bring them to judgement in the infernal courts so that their spirit path may be laid before them.

The idea of horses falling in love with mortal women, or with goddesses, is a constant theme in legend. The queens of powerful kings would act out a mock-ceremony in which they 'married' a sacred horse before the king became invested with power. North American Indian women sometimes really did marry horses! Such a woman would live with it as if it were her husband!

One of the powers of horses is that of fertility, and their holy connection with the sun also links them with the sun-ripened harvest and the golden corn spirit. Horses are also creatures of the moon, and their crescent-shaped shoes are lucky, especially for women. This fertility of both the sun and the moon is celebrated by 'hobby-horses' in May Day revels and ritual dances. The wild horse is also associated with the power of the soul riding forth into the New Year, and festivals at Christmas and Hallowe'en (in ancient times November was New Year's Day or Samhain), which

❧

feature the 'hobby-horse', still remind us of this.

The horse was a symbol of divine power, energy and intelligence. As the unicorn, the horse honed its intelligence until it became pure spirit, a burning spear of gold on its forehead, to lead the beautiful and perfected animal body forward upon the path of sacred wisdom and spiritual enlightenment. The pure white unicorn became a symbol for the eternal spirit, and its connection with the white-horned moon made the white horse a beast of good omen. Abraxus, the dawn horse who pulls the dawn chariot, is associated with happy new beginnings.

Horse skulls and bones were thought to have very powerful magical properties: their skulls were often set upon the gables of houses to give protection and bring good fortune to the family. Old English houses, recently demolished were found to have horse bones implanted in their walls.

Horses were seen as supernatural animals, able to talk to ghosts, fairies and spirits. Witches would try to ride them into the infernal worlds during the night, so that in the morning the poor beasts were exhausted and terrified. To stop the nightly thefts of horses by witches, magical plants, stones with a natural hole through them, and all kinds of blessed charms were hung up over the stable door so that the horses could not be 'hag-ridden'.

Horses can see into the future, and have healing powers. All diseases of the chest and lungs are said to be healed if a person breathes the breath of a horse. Lead a horse through the house, and it will open a pathway for good spirits to live within the home and make it thrive. For a charm to heal the sick, or to drive away bad luck, take three horseshoes and nail them somewhere in the house, 'horns' point-

ing upwards so that you do not 'spill the luck'. Tap each
one with a hammer held in the left hand, and say:

'Father, Son and Holy Ghost, nail the devil to this post,
Thrice smite I with Holy Crook, with this mell I thrice do knock,
One for God, and one for Wod, and one for Lok.'

Fix the hammer across the three horseshoes and it is said
you will have created a barrier so powerful that nothing
evil will be able to pierce it.

If you cross the path of a horse, an old custom advises
you to make a wish.

❧

The Wisewoman's Story
THE HORSEMAN'S WORD

Now this is my story, and this is the way I tell it.

Lord Dorchester once owned a savage and cruel horse
called Cruiser. The animal had already killed three men
and, by the glint in its eye, said Lord Dorchester's groom,
it would kill another three as soon as it could. It seemed
the only thing left to do was to shoot Cruiser.

But then a man of whom many wonders were told came
over from America, one John Rarey, who was famous for
his handling of horses. Yet Cruiser was like nothing he had
ever encountered before.

'That horse is a demon-horse,' said the groom. 'Only one
thing could ever tame it, and that's the old charm they call
the Horseman's Word. It's a magical rune I heard tell of in
my grandmother's day. But it's forgotten now, and Rarey
says he doesn't use magic. He doesn't stand a chance
against Cruiser. The horse will be the death of him.'

'I'm afraid you're right,' said the stable lad, shaking his head sorrowfully as Rarey entered the yard, which was closed off to everyone else.

Rarey stood there alone, not even holding a stick. The stable doors were opened and out rushed Cruiser, ready for the kill! His eyes blazed red and furious as though he truly were a demon horse. He put his head down, showed his great teeth, and charged at Rarey with an unearthly scream. Everyone thought the game was up.

Just before Cruiser was on him, John Rarey put out his hand and said some gentle words in a calm low tone. Cruiser drew sharply to a halt and pawed the ground, his flanks trembling. Rarey approached him, and stroked and patted him. Cruiser relaxed and became sweet and docile.

He never attacked anyone again. But it was a mystery to Lord Dorchester and his stable hands, who had been perched up a ladder watching the scene, what John Rarey had actually said to Cruiser. Rarey never told them. But the groom said ever afterwards that now he knew that John Rarey possessed the secret of the Horseman's Word, and if his old grandmother had been alive, she would have said the same.

And by the light that shines, this story is true!

Nine

DIANA'S OWLS
❦   ❦   ❦

Everybody is familiar with the idea of the 'wise old owl'. These mysterious and beautiful night-time birds are the handmaidens of the goddess of the moon, especially in her guise of Diana, the Egyptian moon goddess, and Athene, the goddess of wisdom and the arts who was worshipped in ancient Greece.

In all the timeless legends of the world, we find that the mother goddess, or the moon goddess, is associated with wisdom. The word 'woman' is said to mean 'the spirit of wisdom'. So Diana's owls, the sacred handmaidens who call through the night with their lonely spirit voices, are privy to the secrets of the past and the future and all the forbidden mysteries of life.

Perhaps it is these bewitching tones which have made people fear the owl through the ages. The Canadian and North American Indians believe that the owl is a bird of deception, and that it can cast evil spells over human souls. The Romans associated the owl with death and disaster, but the Germans considered it a bird of noble magical power, and used an owl's heart and claw, carried under the left armpit, to stave off rabies after being attacked by

a mad dog. This charm was a form of 'sympathetic magic': the people who used it believed that the powers of wisdom and knowledge, whose totem bird was the owl, would keep at bay the negative powers of frenzy and insanity.

Greek soldiers believed that if an owl flew over them or in front of them on a march or in battle, the bird foretold certain victory. If a child in ancient Greece was given the egg of an owl to eat, it was thought that he or she would be safe from becoming a drunkard for life. British people held a similar belief, and broken owl eggs were put into a cup and given to heavy drinkers as a charm to cure their habit. Owl broth was used to cure whooping cough, and salted owl was fed to gout sufferers. Owl eggs, crushed and powdered, were said to cure poor eyesight or blindness.

All over the world the owl was believed to inhabit the

world of spirits, allowing spirit forces to assume an owl shape and flit around the mortal world from time to time. Because of their close communion with spirits, owls were said to foretell births and deaths with their tremulous hooting. They would call when a woman was soon to become pregnant, or even when a romance was ready to bloom! Sometimes, if an owl persistently flew around the house, trying to come in or fluttering down the chimney, it was thought to presage death. If an owl came into the house in Ireland, the poor creature was killed because people thought that, if it was allowed to fly away again, it would take the luck of the house away with it.

Diana the moon goddess sends her owls to tell mothers-to-be that a girl baby, one of the 'spirits of wisdom' is soon to be born to her. This belief was very widespread in France; in Wales, constant hooting and crying of the owls around a village foretold that a girl would have a baby to a man who would not marry her. Diana's owls gave warnings, blessings and tidings to women to help them and protect them.

Because it was associated with the magical powers of women, which could not be understood and explained away by logic, the owl was hated and feared, and people often looked upon it as a bird of ill omen. It was thought to haunt churches and to live in ruins, drinking lamp oil and consorting with ghosts and demon creatures of the night. There was a tradition that if a man looked into the nest of an owl (its secret place of power and symbol of its origin) he would be stricken with melancholy all his life (i.e. his life-forces would ebb away). This strange old belief seems to be related to the idea of a man crossing the powers of

female magic: – not a safe thing to do! A woman, it seemed, was quite safe to peer into as many nests as she liked!

Henry Thoreau, an American writer born at the beginning of the nineteenth century, seemed to sense something of the feminine magic of owls. 'I rejoice that there are owls,' he wrote. 'Wise midnight hags! They represent the stark twilight and unsatisfied thoughts which we all have.' He thought that their cries 'suggested a vast and undeveloped nature which men have not recognized'. Today we would call this 'undeveloped nature' the 'unconscious', that great sea of hidden thought-life and deep, secret feeling from which artistic inspiration and intuition flows. It seems fitting that the moon-goddess's sacred handmaidens should make Henry Thoreau think of such things!

❧

The Wisewoman's Story

DIANA AND HER OWLS

Now this is my story, and this is the way I tell it. There was once a poor young girl who was left quite alone in the world. Her parents had died when she was a baby, and since then her grandmother had taken care of her. But now the old lady was gone, and poor little Bridget had to struggle on alone, taking care of her little cottage, feeding the animals, and tending her grandmother's patch of land all by herself.

Bridget would often feel quite desolate because she had no one to talk to or give her advice. One moonlit night she had a dream that her grandmother was calling to her out in the dark woods. She woke up and ran outside into the silvery night, half believing her dream was real.

She had not walked far into the woods when the full moon broke clear through the clouds and shone in glory upon a little clearing in the trees. There stood the Moon Woman, Diana the Goddess, and around her a hundred owls silently glided, hooting from time to time. In this magical halo of moonlight and owls, the moon goddess walked up to Bridget and greeted her with a smile.

'I want to share one of my secrets with you,' she told

Bridget. 'You must never despair or wonder what to do again. Whenever you need a wise answer to a question which is troubling you, just call out to me, and my owls will answer you. If they hoot once while you count nine off on your fingers, the answer is yes, but if they call twice while you are counting, the answer is no. If they call three times as you count, the question is not ready for an answer, and you must come and ask me again another time. And if my owls don't call out to you at all, why then the problem is something that you can work out wisely yourself.'

Then the Moon Woman kissed little Bridget, and a beam of silver fell from her mouth and slipped onto Bridget's finger in the shape of a shining ring.

'Don't forget, my dear,' said the beautiful goddess, 'you

have only to look for my sign upon the face of my owls, because each one is heart-shaped, and I am mistress of the heart and keeper of its knowledge. The owls will always be your friends, and I will speak to you through them.'

Then suddenly the moon sped behind a cloud, and the Moon Woman was gone. But her owls made phantom shapes in the darkness, soundlessly swooping and looking at little Bridget with their strange rushlight eyes gleaming in the darkness. But Bridget wasn't afraid because she knew they were her friends, and that she would never be alone again.

The Moon Woman's magic is for all to share. Why not put a question or two to the owls, just for fun, and hear what they have to say about it!

Ten

THE DUN COW

❧   ❧   ❧

The French say that cows have sweet breath because a compassionate cow saw Jesus shivering in the manger, and was moved to warm him with her breath and draw hay over him as a coverlet. Ever since, according to legend, a cow's breath has been wholesome and healing, and she has carried her calf for nine months, in harmony with human mothers.

The great goddess Hathor of ancient Egypt often appeared to mortals in the guise of a cow, and the cow is also very important in British mythology. She is one of the spirit animals which guide and protect the souls of men and women. In India the cow is sacred, and it is believed she can absorb and harmonize negative and evil forces and vibrations. In England the Milky Way was sometimes called 'cow's lane', because whoever gave a cow to help the poor would be guided by that same cow along the treacherous 'soul road' after death and safely led into the sanctuary of paradise. To the Celts, the ancient people of Britain, cattle were sacred, and both the cow and the bull were holy beasts.

Cattle are said to live in close spiritual sympathy with

their owners, sharing the happiness and the sorrows of the family. There is a tradition that cattle turn to the east and kneel as the clock strikes midnight on Christmas Eve, to greet the coming of the Christ-child. They also talk among themselves at this magical hour, predicting the fate of their owners and the community in the coming year.

In Wales the family would go to the byre on Twelfth Night (which once used to be Christmas Day) and drink a toast to each ox in cider or ale, speaking the name of the animal as they did so. A cake with a hole through the middle was hung on the horn of the oldest ox, and the family watched to see what he would do. If he tossed it off his horn at once, that was a lucky sign. If not, the family would prompt him to do so by tickling or prodding, and the mistress of the house would stand before him, and someone who took the part of the bailiff, behind him. According to the direction in which he tossed the cake and who caught it, the fortune of the family would be good or bad.

There are many stories in Europe of fairy cattle. These were sometimes little creatures, no bigger than small dogs, who pastured on the fairy raths or hills. They could appear as a single spirit animal, pure white or strangely coloured even a striking sea green or lavender! These creatures would graze with a farmer's regular herd, giving warning of major events in the life of the family and the community. But sometimes the fairy cow would be a giantess, coming in times of need to supply a plentiful flow of milk for the poor and the starving, until human greed and abuse drove her away. Occasionally the fairy cow appears as an aggressor, a huge and threatening presence which challenges the bravery of certain heroes and protectors. Guy of Warwick, for instance, had to slay a monster cow to bring peace to the land – the cow who, not long before, had been a benign and generous creature freely giving her milk to nourish the people.

The earth goddess of whom the cow is a magical sign, often appears in this two fold guise: first nourisher and protector, and then a malignant force, flinging her young out of the nest to fend for themselves. The aim of this alarming change of attitude is to teach her children who would otherwise remain crippled and stunted in their growth by their dependence on her, to grow up and look after themselves.

At certain times, too, the fairy cow appears as phantom beast, ready to lead a soul away from its earthly home into paradise. Such a fairy cow is the protecting animal-angel who will take the human soul down the 'cow's path' or

'soul bridge' of the Milky Way, which leads from earth to the heavenly worlds, and which is beset with dangers and pitfalls that the cow can be relied upon to ward off.

When cows low to one another across the fields, stormy, boisterous weather is predicted. When they low at night, persistently and in unison, a snowy winter is foretold. When they feed all together in an absorbed and determined manner, or lie down, rain is coming; but if they stand or rest in the highest point of the field, fine weather is coming to stay.

'Dun' refers to the brown markings on a cow or a bull, but it is also a Celtic word meaning 'court' or 'royal'. The 'dun cow' of the wisewoman's story is no doubt a brown cow, but the word also suggests her royal heritage as a sacred creature of the heavenly courts!

❧

The Wisewoman's Story
THE TALE OF THE DUN COW

Now this is my story, and this is the way I tell it.

Once upon a time there fell upon the moorland folk of Lancashire a terrible and dread famine, the like of which had never been known before. It persisted so long that the people had to draw a little blood from their famished and skeleton thin sheep and cattle and feed it to their children, just to keep them alive.

The moorland folk were near despairing, when one night a great comet flicked its tail in the starry heavens, and burned out due west of the moor. 'It's a sign,' said one of the village women whom some called a wisewoman. 'Something will happen to make things better.'

'It's a sign all right,' said another woman . . . only *her* they called a witch. 'A sign that things will go from bad to worse.'

The next day such a strange and marvellous sight met their eyes that the moorland folk were ready to think they had gone mad. A huge cow, as big as a house, wandered up and down the lanes, peaceably cropping the scarce grass. Yet where she munched, the vegetation sprung up as green and moist as that in a rich and fertile valley. What was more, she allowed herself to be milked by whoever approached her. But whenever the milk pail was full, she gently moved away and stood waiting quietly and kindly

for the next hungry villager to come and milk her.

'That is what we must do,' said the wisewoman at once, 'we must be careful to take only one pail of milk each day for every person, or we'll drive the holy beast away, and our blessing and good fortune with her.'

Everybody agreed, and life went on wonderfully for a time, and no one was unhappy or wanting.

But this wasn't enough for the old woman they called a witch. She must find a way to get more than her fair share. And so she whittled and worried and wondered until she worked out a plan.

She went up to the beautiful dun cow as usual the next morning to claim her pailful of milk. But instead of using her wooden pail, she brought a bunch of deep kettles, which she hid behind her back. And she brought forth a big sieve, and said to the dun cow, 'Good morning, my lady; and here's my pretty new pail, if you please.' Then she set about milking the dun cow into the sieve, only she put one of the kettles beneath it, and when that was full, she pushed it out of the way and grabbed another, carrying on until that was full, and so on and so on.

When she was filling her seventh kettle, the wisewoman walked by. 'If you don't let the poor creature be this very instant,' she said, 'our lovely dun cow will never forgive you.'

'Oh fiddlesticks!' said the witch, and kept on milking. At that moment there was a great twinkling in the air as though a star had fallen plumb to earth in broad daylight, and the dun cow was nowhere to be seen. The witch's cruel greed had driven her away forever.

But thanks to the wisewoman's prayers, the grass grew lush and green once again wherever the dun cow had fed, and the crops in the valley grew too, and the animals flourished instead of sickening and dying, as they had before the coming of the beautiful dun cow. The people continued happy and prosperous. But when they thought of the starvation and want and misery, they thought of the witch's unkindness and greed. And when they thought of peaceful, prosperous days and happy, carefree times, they thought of the good wisewoman and her lessons of gratitude, sharing and kindness. And the dun cow smiled to herself in the starry fields of paradise, because the people had heeded her teaching well.

THE RAVEN
❦ ❦ ❦

Legend relates how ravens were once as white as swans, and similar in size, but how one day a raven told Apollo that Coronis, a Thessalian nymph whom the sun god adored, was inconstant. Apollo shot the nymph with his dart; he hated the tell-tale bird who had broken his heart and his romantic dream so much that according to Ovid:

'He blacked the raven o'er and bid him prate in his white plumes no more.'

❦

Ever since, ravens have become as dark angels, bearing the wisdom and the secrets of life and death, foretelling wars and disasters and the mortality of warriors.

Ravens are seen also as emblems of God's providence. They fed Elijah in the wilderness, and St Paul the Hermit was also sustained by them. In Christian art he is depicted with a raven who is bringing him a loaf of bread, the 'bread of life'. St Oswald holds in his hand a raven who has brought him the ring of truth, and St Benedict has a raven at his feet, symbol of the journey of life. In the Denham Tracts it is reported that Sir John Duck, a wealthy burgher

of Durham living in the seventeenth century, set up his fortune and position in life by means of a piece of silver that was dropped at his feet by a raven.

In Norse mythology, Odin was attended by two sacred ravens, Hugin and Munin (mind and memory). Each day these birds flew all over the world, returning to Odin's shoulders at night to whisper into his ears what they had seen and heard.

The 'fatal raven', consecrated to Odin of Woden, the Nordic god of wisdom and victory, was the emblem on the Danish standard. This raven was reputed to be possessed of necromantic power (the themes of prophesy and death again occurring in connection with the raven).

The tame ravens kept at the Tower of London are tidings of the fortune of the country. If these birds are ever lost, or fly away, it is said that the Crown will fall and Britain will be doomed.

❧

The Wisewomans's Story

THE STOLEN EGG

Now this is my story, and this is the way I tell it.

There was once a little farmhouse up on the Yorkshire

moors, Top Withens it was called, my dear. An old place it was, blown higgledy-piggledy with the wind, and all its stonework gnarled like an old tree. Many a ghost had passed through its halls, and many a fay had danced before its door. But it was a cosy place for all that, and in the year of this my story, it had a mother, a baby and a father, and a little lad and lass besides who were near each other in age, being nine and ten years old, the lad the elder of the two.

One blue and white spring evening, when the sunshine was as deep and rich as a patch of marigolds, young Tom took out of his pocket a large pale egg and showed it to his sister.

'Is that a pullet's egg?' the innocent asked, eyeing it curiously.

'It's nobbut a raven's egg' said Tom proudly. 'I've just fetched it from the nest in the old oak by Roe Crag. It's still warm see? I'm going to hatch it and have a raven to myself, and teach it to talk.'

His sister Mercy made no answer, but she thought to herself that no good would come of it. Her own dear mother was too sensible a woman to frighten her with tales of the Great Black Bird who carried off the wicked. But she had heard tell of it from the village children down in the valley, and that made her afraid of the great flapping ravens with their shrewd glittering eyes. She had heard another story too, and it was a terrible one . . .

The very next day dawned cold, stormy and wet. The cuckoo they had heard all week stopped singing. And worst of all, as they sat by the fire, built up to a roar because it was so chilly, the baby began to wail as loud as the keening wind.

'What ails the baby, mother?' asked Mercy fearfully. But her mother shook her head in her anxiety, and told her that the bairn was running a fever. Then Mercy knew what she had heard was true: that a baby died for every egg stolen from a raven's nest. So she took the egg out of her brother's inside pocket where he was keeping it warm as he dozed before the fire, and slipped out into the wintry blast of the night.

Oh the wind was wild, my dear, and the furies were in heaven. But all through the brewing storm she struggled, up to the old oak hard by Roe Crag. How menacing the great tree looked in the darkness and the flitting glimpses of moonlight as the dark clouds swallowed up the moon and spat her out again, the raven's oak with some of its topmost branches lightning-stricken. But bravely Mercy began to climb, and she neither hesitated nor looked down until she came to the great nest snug amongst the boughs. There she took the precious egg from her handkerchief and placed it carefully in the nest. Just at that moment the raven came home to roost, and settled on the branch in front of her.

Oh, he was a black thing, my dear, and a big thing, with shining, shining eyes, sharp and clear as stars. And he croaked once, twice, thrice. Then his mate joined him, and they both sat upon the branch, staring, staring at Mercy, who thought her time was up, and the Great Black Bird had come in double, the better to get her. But then of a sudden, she found that she could understand the bird-language, because the ravens were talking to her.

'You are wise, Mercy, child of your mother,' said the male raven. 'You have done well to bring us back our egg, the cherished egg of our hearts. Let us show you what lies within.'

And Mercy looked, and she beheld a ring of light inside the egg. And the light showed her Roe Crag, and a great king sleeping in the hollow hill, with forty white knights asleep next to forty white steeds. And the king's horse was the whitest of all, as white as an angel's wings.

'That is King Arthur, and his knights of the Round Table' croaked the female raven.

'When all the world cries out in its deepest peril, these men will rise and ride out to fight the last great battle against darkness. Mercy, daughter of your father, understand that each and every egg of the raven folk might be the very egg that bears the enchanted bird that will rouse Arthur and his knights from their sleep – the egg that contains the soul of King Arthur himself. Now do you see why an innocent babe wails in sorrow and dies of a broken heart whenever an egg is stolen?'

'We do not wish it so' said the father raven. 'But yet it is so. We are darkness, guardians of the Secret, and hidden in darkness must we keep it, until the time is right'. And as he finished speaking, the ravens took her, one arm each upon their strong wings, and bore her home. And when she came again into the bosom of her family, they were silent and never asked where she had been, because the grand mark of the wise was upon her. And from that day on, she grew to be a Woman of Power, one who could speak the language of the birds and talk to the beasts, and one who nobly justified her name.

And this story is true, my dear, because my grandmother told it to me.

❧   ❧   ❧